THE HIGH PLACE

THE HIGH PLACE

Lisa St Aubin de Terán

JONATHAN CAPE
THIRTY-TWO BEDFORD SQUARE LONDON

Por la gente

First published 1985
Copyright © by Lisa St Aubin de Terán 1985
Illustrations copyright © by Charles Shearer 1985
Jonathan Cape Ltd, 32 Bedford Square, London WC1B 3EL

British Library Cataloguing in Publication Data

St Aubin de Terán, Lisa
The high place.
I. Title
821'.914   PR6069.T13

ISBN 0-224-02813-8

Printed in Great Britain by
Ebenezer Baylis & Son Ltd
The Trinity Press, Worcester and London

Contents

Preface

The people in this poem were the workers on the Hacienda el Hatico (the High Place), where I lived for seven years, near Mendoza Fría in Venezuela. The poem is a memorial to those who have died, and a tribute to those who are still living. The notes at the end explain one or two allusions which may be unclear, and the English sense of a few Spanish words. I have used the rhythm in the syllabic metre of the poem in the hope of reproducing something of the naturalness and formality of the archaic high Spanish of Andean speech.

Norfolk,
June 1985   *Lisa St Aubin de Terán*

Prologue

The first strangers to the valley
    came for gold, but found only
        Indians and their scorn;
        and then they settled
        there, sheltering from the sun
            and the dank
festering of the lowland swamps,
    and planted corn and
dragged the great hacienda[1] to its dawn.

The second grain to seed, nearly
    two centuries on, was frail
        coffee, shaded by fruit
        and palm across the
        terraced hills. Then the sugar
            came, with its
own tyranny of roller blades
    and wheel, needing the
twelve best men for each new molienda.[2]

This skilled crew turned the new cut cane
    from flecked juice and scum to the
        blocks of brown sugar made
        from the beaten trays,
        and bound with fibre and packed
            at the mill.
Sometimes, waiting stacks fermented
    in the sun, so the
huge trapiche[3] worked and ground in shifts.

Eight hours of sweat and four of rest
for days on end; and the hordes
of workers, tormented
by fatigue, fuelled
the furnaces and ladled
the froth and
panned and stirred, their eyes blurred with sleep.
All the best loaders
lost a thumb to the cruel cane-crusher.

Its heedless cogs tore off a strip
of living flesh to mark their
rule, initiating
chosen slaves. There was
blood in the sugar and blood
on the land:
where the peasants survived despite
the odds, and some thrived
though they lived scarcely better than dogs.

The difference was their honour
and their pride, and a sense of
history, and also,
the will to laugh and
feel a natural part of things.
They drudged from
six to six, six days a week and
on the seventh day
they drank, and life was like that, always.

There were thirty-two families
on the hacienda. Some lived
so far away over
the crests that they were
seen only on feast days and
to share their
harvests as half-croppers on the
hills. Most, though, lived near
the casa grande⁴ and served the cane.

These fell under the spell of Juan
Moreno, the foreman who
managed all the workers
and whose word was law,
under the higher rule of
el patrón,
Don César, under the last law,
of nature, which was
the cruellest master of them all.

The miche⁵ helped the wounds to heal
and the sun to rise, and the
night to come and end for
a while the tending
of the hacienda and all
the thin graves –
of poor green Capino and old
Florencia and
Josefa and all of the others:

13

the sons and wives and mothers whose
    names became part of the fields
        and flowers. With death so
            close by, no one was
        allowed to die completely –
            they were all
    there in the evenings and in the
        hushed places, with their
life's mark carved on to other faces.

Theirs was a universal face,
    stamped with pain, like part of the
        mill's conveyor belt filled
            with resigned sunken
        eyes, their lids cast downwards by
            hopelessness.
Only children showed any real
        surprise; the others
knew that they would lose despite their pride.

Was that why they idolised dead
    children, making them angels[6]
        for their innocence and
            games and dreams? But though
        they died angels, their narrow
            backs were bent
by labour and the strap, their lips
        were cracked by thirst and
dust: these children of the tearless grief.

Satin wings were stitched to the robe
over their usual rags
and they were buried in
a circus of mirth,
with a refusal to mourn
their release
from the sure hazard of their birth.
The wheel groaned and wheezed,
death followed dearth, and the children laughed.

And laughter could always be heard
on the High Place, between the
village of Mendoza
and the old town of
Mototán, squeezed between the
sugar and
the tears. Then, down on the lower
slopes, the rows of squat
avocado groves appeared and grew.

Nothing had changed for a hundred
years. The workers accepted
all the calamities
just like a mother
accepts her family and
still finds time
to smile. There would be drinking and
singing and the hours
of thinking, and the whetstones and fights.

15

And everyone's nerves were flayed and
displayed there on the High Place.
They all knew where they were
and stayed – proud of their
power to withstand hurt and
proud of their
inherited purgatory and
of their mastery
of the land which passed from hand to hand.

I

Josefa Perez

(Who lived nearest the casa grande, and was married to
the goatherd, and died of old age in 1972)

Josefa lived in a blackened
   shack and served coffee like hot
      mud from her greasy range
      half-way up the hill
   behind the avocados
      and the stream,
pinned between Juan's barbed-wire frontier
   and the Terán palms
planted at the birth of every male.

They were a dying history of
   fibre-nut withering on
      her swept doorstep, as words
         shrivelled in her mouth.
   Only Natividad, her
      sad husband,
   could unwind her memories to
      the wasted inner
core of bone sieved through his own wheezing.

Josefa knew and culled every
   whisper of gossip that slipped
      and drifted through the grass,
         the pink tasselled hill
   scrub which she called her own, since
      it would grow
high over her grave: a scant wedge
   of Mendoza with
Josefa Perez there on the stone.

19

Josefa had hair like beaten
   sugar strands, scorched limbs, and breasts
   flattened by time and births.
    For the plantation
  owners there were rows of palms.
     Josefa
recalled a death roll of her own:
   Juan, Chucho, Bébe,
Sara, Ramona, el Cojo, Luis . . .

'And then there were' . . . and she would scowl,
  searching the cracks of her dry
   wizened skull for names for
   the nameless who were
  dead, and only María
     is left now.
But from the roll-call of her womb
  she retraced her sons,
filling enamel mugs with sour dregs.

II

María

(Who was slow-witted and unloved and abused,
and usually blocked the path from the sugar-mill to the
hill)

So only María was there,
    who stayed alone, rooted to
    the two doors of her shack,
        staked to the lintel
    that her father made and the
        mesh gate to
keep their annual pig back. She was
        María, who had
grown tired of standing on the dirt track,

    waiting sadly for her man to
    come for her, anxious for her
    babies to be born: el
        Bobo's babies from
    the five times that he lured her
        from her home
and sent her back, thick and shameless
    to her father's shack.
People said that Bobo didn't care.

    They said it was his mule he loved.
    María knew that, knew it
    as she knew her womb would
        sag. So she spent her
    time gathering coffee beans
        like red slugs
of ripe Borbón,[7] and her father's
    pockmarked corn; spread it
and then crushed it with a hollowed stone.

Then she ground and brewed it to the
    muddy scum they drank and nursed
        at old Natividad's.
        Crazed María fetched
    the kindling while Josefa
        raised her spawn:
five live children for those ancient
    skirts, and more each time
el Bobo came and used their daughter.

But Bobo, faithful to his mule,
    came only once a year like
        Easter, to refill her
        womb. She was crazy,
    and he didn't care if she
        died waiting.
So she cobbled her frayed skirts to
    her and never cried,
just stared at the sun and stroked her hair

on the path to the flea patch, and
    the mat, where she slept in a
        huddle in the hut, with
        the smoke and her five
    children, and their lice, and her
        father, who
grieved for the pain, and Josefa,
    mother of the grey
coffee, who loved them come drought come rain.

III

Señor Juan Moreno

(Who was foreman of the hacienda, much respected,
but who had grown bitter in his old age)

Juan passed María every day,
  at six and six he watched her
    grow and fade, easy prey
      but stale since Bobo
  had her. That mule was sick; he
      had no time.
He was in love and had more things
    on his mind than red
ants in the fields, and times were changing.

Juan was never a modern man,
  so his sad mouth was crumpled,
    and a line sewn for each
      year of furrows filled
  and spoiled, and eighty years of
      grief and toil
  marked on his tired jaw. That was how
    he seemed at first, but
the workers knew that he had power.

He was gaunt in his working clothes,
  limping slightly from the hill;
    always the first to come,
      always last to go.
  Señor Juan to other men,
      el Capo
  to the workers, as his father
    had been before him
on the upper lip of the high slope.

And Juan lived, like his father, in
   a long shack with three dark rooms
      and a space for guinea
         pigs between them. One
   more room than old Josefa.
         And his own
enclosure and a lemon tree
      to guard the threadbare
path that led up to his papered hut.

He had crimson capachos,[8] and
   clumps of pink begonias
      in rusted milk tins; and
         thin grey pigs who dragged
      their bellies in the dirt and
         dogs and hens
and a young wife to scratch his yard
      with a real broom and
not just twigs forced through a sardine tin.

There was no fish-coloured ring that
   other women used, Lord no,
      señor Juan was a man
         to be reckoned with.
   He oversaw the workers,
         earned twice their
wage, and took home almost enough
         to eat meat every
day: sausage and chicken with his beans,

sardines with his egg, rice with his
plantains, rum with his Toddy.[9]
Nobody questioned Juan's
power. With four cows
he could retire, people said,
with four cows
he was rich. But he kept going:
a part of the past.
The mill-wheel would unwind without him.

And he knew that the streams would flood,
and the dirt tracks grow over,
slopes would crumble, woods burn,
coffee die, cane spoil.
That was why Juan toiled, with his
harsh whisper
that the men obeyed. He inspired
fear and respect, he
had el Patrón's ear, and the same pride.

And he had weak lungs, broken teeth,
soft food, a green suede hat, and
toes like talons in his
woven shoes. Señor
Juan kept his sheathed machete
on his hip
all day from six to six. His fights
were over, he was
accepted as a man of honour.

He'd tried and won, if winning was
  his stretch of scrub and his four
    cows out on the hill with
      milk to sell; and aches
  in his bare ribs that racked him
      in the night,
and the sight of his own children
    dying as they had
before, when he was young: nothing changed.

But señor Juan was never a
  modern man, nor one to whine
    when time stood still and robbed
      him. His house was like
  the frontier to the hills with
      parakeets,
blue birds, orchids and inmortelles.[10]
    Every outcrop had
a tale to tell, and Juan knew them all.

When dusk came, drawing his bastard
  sons in: three generations
    scattered across the hills,
      he would drink coffee
  and spit chimó[11] in a tarred
      pool of stain
round his stool and brood on bad times
    and his torn breath and
the old insult of his mother's death.

IV

Old Florencia

(Who was Juan Moreno's mother, and lived for over a
hundred years on the High Place, where she was denied
a proper coffin)

There wasn't a stick of cane on
　　the whole hacienda that could
　　　let him forget her wrong.
　　He told her virtues
　first, her hundred years, then he
　　　told the crime:
'Because[12] of her age, and marriage,
　　and because she lived
harried all her drudged and weary days.'

Florencia, who slaved for a
　pittance and her burial,
　　had died in faith. And not
　a grain of sand would
have disputed her right to
　　a coffin
fit for a queen, and a place in
　　the chill patchwork of
narrow graves at Mendoza Fría.

Only that last journey mattered.
　But when she died, el Patrón
　　was away, and his wife
　　had denied her a
　proper coffin, although for
　　ten decades
of selfless toil she had dressed in
　　ragged black, and bowed
her neck, trusting in that final box,

33

adorned with all the luxuries
that she had denied herself
in life. A hundred years
of sacrifice for
a silk-lined, polished box with
brass handles.
How many times had she not closed
her eyes and seen it?
The best carved box in all the Andes!

Instead a hotchpotch box was made
and spurned, since Juan refused it;
and there was only one
day left till her nose
turned green and vultures circled
in raw sun
over her gut. That day, Juan, her
eldest son, begged for
help from house to house and don to don.

El Patrón's cousins helped him out,
and he bought a fine coffin
and arranged a good wake,
but not all the rum
and candles could repair his
dented faith.
Her worn bones were shamed, though she would
never know what her
mistress stinted or her neighbours spent.

It was Juan's own stone to carry:
  his gall and grudge. His best friend,
    Ciega,[13] across the way,
      said it brought cancer
to brood and hate. Was that what
       the pain was
in his lung? Perhaps, God willing,
    it would not be long.
Meanwhile his bare creed kept him going.

V

Juan's Wife, Zara

(Who arrived from nowhere, and eloped from the casa grande at the age of fifteen. The other workers never quite forgave her for her lack of history.)

Juan's young wife was known as Zara,
  Zara what? and Zara who?
    Nobody knew. She had
      arrived and stayed, years
    back, with two print frocks and a
        load of junk.
Juan had loved her plump arms from the
      start, washing linen
at the casa grande. 'Wild Zara',

Natividad used to call her,
  and la Ciega said she was
    'not quite there'. That was who
      Juan fell in love with,
    and stole in his dotage from
        the laundry
of the casa grande, away
      to a one-room love
nest behind the rumbling sugar-mill.

Toads and lizards clung to their damp
  walls under a canopy
    of ferns and lichen; and
      young Zara calmed her
    manic laughter and grew big
        with Mano
Negro, while Juan limped his way back
      and forth from the cane
to his bridal shack and his Zara.

The people of the hacienda
said he must be mad, Zara
had even made him build
a bed! Zara had
bewitched poor Juan: she filled his
billycan
with mortadella, and rubbed his
grizzly hair with strange
oils, and bandaged up his every scratch

with plantain fibres, and she strewed
their hut with aromatic
leaves and graveyard flowers
and nobody, not
even la Ciega, who was
old and blind,
slept in a bed! What were mats and
hammocks for? Zara
must be mad, or so the workers said.

Later, the scandal settled, and
life went on. Zara never
spoke to certain neighbours
and their children were
all instructed in the feud.
Otherwise,
the cane was cut and the juice boiled,
and the sugar packed
and stacked and graded beside the shed.

Zara bore Juan four sons and a
　wild and stubborn daughter, a
　　stunted child who plagued them
　　　as Juan grew old and
　　tired, and Zara herself grew
　　　　worn and set,
　with her strange meats and her lilies
　　　and the much scorned bed,
her wayward girl, and her last son, dead.

VI

Juan Moreno's heirs

(Who were his four sons: Mano Negro, Goyo, Nesto and Capino, and his capricious daughter, Coromoto)

So señor Juan, in his old age,
    had these five heirs. The eldest
    and darkest was Mano
        Negro, known too as
    Antonio José, who
            carried his
quick Indian blood hot in his
        temper night and day.
He was always ready to die and

ready to kill, for his dour pride
    only, and a prickly rage.
    He drank himself rabid
        on his first wage, and
    then continued drinking the
            same sour cane
with little change: Mano Negro
    had the black hand of
death marked in his face – he would die young.

Zara feared he'd die in a fight
    and never make use of his
        skills as mechanic and
        carter, and rarer
    still as the best grafter since
            Don César
himself. If tongues clicked behind his
    back, nobody spoke
a word out of turn to Juan's son's face.

45

Not with his temper. His brother
    Nesto, and his squat sister
    Moto, at least gave in
        to the stick; but then,
    Mano Negro was spoiling
        to die young.
Not even the avocados
        could make him stay straight:
he'd be killed in a brawl any day.

Coromoto, known as Moto,
    was 'ñor Juan's only daughter.
    She lived in a dream. It
        had always been so.
It was Zara's dream really,
        Zara's fault
that Moto would never 'do' for
        service: too proud to
be told, with her pig-head and her pets.

It was rumoured that she wouldn't
    eat her guinea pigs. And she
    even wore ribbons in
        her frizzy hair. Juan
    said it wasn't fair that his
        young sons should
be pretty while Moto reigned so
        plain. Mad María
teased her for her ugliness and airs.

46

But Moto was too locked in her
     self to care. It divided
       her home when she refused
         to help. Juan beat her
     and Zara wept, but Moto
           had her dreams.
She dreamt of wearing dresses to
     the ground with fifteen
veils to trail across the inmortelles.

Years passed, and Moto failed to grow
     or reach her puberty, though
       her tinned plants spread and bloomed
         brighter than any
     valley in the hills. She and
           her brothers
guarded them from the pigs and hens.
     And she fantasised
about sex and her chances to sin.

Nesto had his mother's fair hair
     mixed with Juan's purple hue to
       give a sallow tone that
         pleased no one. It was
     his lot to be ignored. What
           could he do
to compete with his more extreme
           family? So he
chewed cane stalks and was silently bored.

He was like Coromoto's slave,
he, and Goyo, her other
page. Goyo fell in love
with a girl he saw
in church at a funeral.
He was eight,
and she was a planter's daughter:
la niña Dulce –
he prayed for her till his knuckles ached.

And he thought of her when he rubbed
out the cane hairs from his back,
and when Juan battered him
when the pigs got out,
or Moto teased him when he
spilled his food,
and when Zara chided him when
he was rude. One day,
la niña Dulce would admire him.

Goyo believed this in his bones,
it was a part of him. When
Capino died, niña
Dulce wept for him.
She'd had real tears in her eyes.
On his mat,
once, Goyo woke up wet and full
of love for Moto
but they all beat him when he said so.

That was why he prayed for niña
   Dulce, who was prettier
    and kind: poor Moto looked
     like a witch sometimes.
   When he had tantrums, they ducked
       him in brine.
   But Goyo strove to survive his
      trials until such
time as he could buy his Dulce's love.

VII

Capino, the Green Boy

(Who was Juan's favourite child, and died after being
prescribed copper sulphate instead of Epsom salts)

Capino was the last of Juan's
    five heirs, child of his old age,
      born the year his rib–cage
        cracked and his eyes glazed
  under cataracts, edging
          towards the
other blind. He could bear not to
      see, but not to lose
a child in such pointless agony.

The baby brought new hope into
    their peeling hut. Juan took him
      to the cane fields daily,
        parading his new
  son to all his men, whittling
          bamboo toys
for him – he would have everything.
      Then, he grew sick, and
Juan was broken by the sight of it.

He nursed Capino, now aged four,
    stilled his thin fingers and his
      swollen glands, and stroked his
        tallow hair and watched
  his pain grow worse despite the
          poultices:
verdolaga[14] and kaolin.
      When potions failed, a
bitter eye had surely made a curse?

53

Juan knew the witch man over the
hill, past Mendoza Fría.
He took Capino there,
described his worms and
diarrhoea. The drunken
Brujo sighed
and prescribed poison crystals for
the clear water eyes
that would accuse Juan's grief till he died.

Juan bought the poison, and forced it
down Capino's throat till he
was sick. Juan hit him and
gave him more until
his favourite choked, and then
he forbore.
All night long he cried, all night long
while the geckos kept
their guard. By dawn his blond son was green:

green like plantains with their sheeted
palms, grey-green as sugar leaves,
blue willow-green; ochre
like escoba[15] and
araguäney;[16] and the whites
of his eyes
were light sage like a plump lizard's
belly. His fair hair
lay like stalks of crushed grass under cane.

Capino passed that day into
the mountain myth, changed from Juan's
last love-child to the green
boy. For Juan, counting
still with his fingers, it was
hard to say
how much of the caustic crystal
was inside his boy
and how much spilt out in the pigswill.

From the hill to the hospital –
that was no better than a
barracks, an abattoir –
Capino sicked up
his rat poison in the cart.
'Will I die?'
he asked his father. Sick on the
floor and on his feet:
copper sulphate to drive home the shaft.

Copper sulphate to destroy his
flesh. 'Will I die?' Juan could kill
the witch, break his neck with
his own machete.
But who could save his green boy
purged by death?
'Will I die?' No one dared tell him,
'Yes.' 'Will I die?' he
asked from his far end of the drab ward.

Zara dripped wet cotton wool on
  his lips, and Juan hovered near
    and wept; and then limped back
      to his decaying
shack, to wait for the signal.
        How many
coffins had he carried down the
    hill? He didn't know,
his fingers had run out, years ago.

Capino, at four, would die an
  angel, so no one else would
    weep for him. Zara would
      prop open his lids
with thorns so the child might see
      his maker.
The undertaker would stitch stiff
    shining wings to his
gown, and the children would sing for him.

'Will I die?' said the green boy. 'Will
  I die?' He asked for a week,
    while black blood leaked out from
      his bladder and his
lips cracked in their whispered guess.
        'Will I die?'
Yes. And no one would mention the
    hushed-up rat poison
or the newspaper[17] stuffed in the mess.

VIII

Eladio

(Who had water on the brain, and believed that if he
saw an eagle, he would get better)

No one had ever seen eagles
  over the hacienda, not
    even Florencia
      in her hundred years.
  Juan told Eladio this
        in vain; there
was a cloud like a small sack of
    clotted blood inside
Eladio's brain, and emptiness.

Only the air held his head up.
  Meanwhile, his ten children starved
    on the gruel shared from
      Eladio's one
  enamel cup, chipped and worn
        to a film
round the handle. Rice water and
    banana soup were
the only fuel for their growing mouths.

They nagged for food while their father
  was away on the hills and
    their mother was tired out
      from trying to scrub
a living off the dirt patch
        el Patrón
gave her while Eladio's hurt
      healed. He had once been
the best end–ladler in the valley.

And he'd had more sugar to his
   tally than all the new boys
      put together: now he
         was a sky gazer
   and hydrocephalic and
         prey to the
weather, drenched by the rain and hail,
      defying his strange
lot, scouring the clouds for an eagle.

   His wife had substituted air
      for water, switching the two
         elements inside her
            ruined husband's head.
      While she slaved, he stared. Her nails
            were grazed, her
fingers bled, her bones ached. At first,
         she had thought it was
easy to go mad – skive work, eat free.

   She would have welcomed such a fate.
      But after the first sour years,
         she left her hate scrabbled
            in with the bitten
      seeds in the dust. Her children
            would never
come to much, stunted from birth and
         driven early to
work. Let him stare for her misery:

60

It was all invested in his
   deeds. She had carried his weight
    for eight years of sickness.
     She craved his vacant
company and kept the grains
     from the drear
gruel for him. He alone had
    escaped work. He had
air on the brain, a halo – power.

Like the second Messiah, his
   was the rarest power of
    not being there. His wife
    knew that the others
   treated him as an omen:
     when he was
out there on the crags, braving death
    and waiting for his
bird, all was right, despite his madness.

Time took the scorn from his former
   uselessness and restored his
    honour. When years passed and
    still he didn't deign
  to disturb his own silence,
    he became
almost a deity like the
    plaster saints, and he
was one of them in a higher sphere.

Juan knew that there was no place on
    the hacienda for the likes
    of Eladio – a
        wageless worker who
    wouldn't work, who enlisted
        then wandered,
leaving his ditch or weeding line
    without a word of
excuse, and there were no excuses.

Yet, somehow, Eladio was
    allowed to stay on the land,
        unmolested even
            by stones, and no one
    mocked his gaunt bones, not even
            Juan rebuked
him. Eladio had air on
    the brain. Disciple
of the wind and rain, and an eagle.

When the black beans ran through him in
    a ceaseless stream of cramping
        diarrhoea, and the
            sun crazed his bare head
    and the wind cracked his glazed stare,
            he didn't
care. His eyes were on the Highlands
    wanting to fly: if
the bird came, he would be sane again.

IX
Abigäíl

(Who nearly killed herself by spreading scandal)

Abigäíl lived in an old
       moated house with scrubbed flagged floors,
       not dirt, but stone. Only
          the casa grande
       could rival her spotless home.
          Her four grown
sons never once got drunk within
       spitting distance of
their fierce mother, such was their respect.

'Bigäíl lived like a painted
       saint, with her home arranged like
       an altar, and her sons
          for flowers. Even
     . her daughter wore white frills like
             Don César's
daughters; she knew their house inside,
          down to the dolls' room
under the green stairs, and put on airs.

When she married, she would have goats
       and mats. She was the only
       work–child to go to mass.
          And she wore made shoes
       and went to school behind old
             Cal'chano's
where she deciphered papers and
          came home with ideas
worse than Moto's and with pulled red ears.

Where the teacher hit her, she was
   still a peasant under the
      frills and always would be.
         It was a mystery
      how her father got his start
         years ago
   as a medianero;[18] but
      he produced his sacks
of corn and his fat profit each year.

And now, with an ox plough to hire,
   what could stop him? They'd grown too
      grand for the hacienda.
         He and his boys still
      had to bring their skills to the
         molienda.
But when the furnaces were killed
   and the wheel bound, they
were free to till their own fields of crops,

so long as they shared the yield with
   Don César, and free to tend
      their gaudy shrine and feel
         superior and
      lock their gates. They had few friends
         or neighbours
on the hacienda who could stand
      'Bigäíl's loose tongue.
She had a mind like caustic soda.

She would lean there on her gate and
    promise certain ruin to
      her peers, and nothing could
        stop her from gloating.
      Even Juan, who was almost
          her cousin
  and had grown mild in his old age,
        said he'd wring her neck.
Her husband begged and pleaded with her:

'We have everything, 'Bigäíl,
    why spoil it with this slander?
      The wheel always turns and
        we have to survive
  by standing by each other.'
        Not she, though.
  Abigäíl lived and breathed by
        leaning on her gate
and venting spite, that was her downfall.

And it came as no surprise to
    the workers when someone crept
      into her spotless yard
        and drove a butcher's
    cleaver through her head, leaving
        her for dead.
  Nor were they surprised when this scourge
        of the hacienda
and mud-raker of their lives survived.

No, they just sighed and kept going;
    'Weeds never die,' they said. But
        Abigäíl went to
        the National Guard
    and she tried to accuse half
        her neighbours.
When she returned, bandaged and still
        unlearned, the battle
lines were drawn: they would not buy her corn.

It was Juan who made her grieved spouse
    choose – send her away or lose
        his land. Unless she was
        gone by the next moon,
    they'd burn his whole house down with
        no recourse
to the law now – no National Guard
        could stop a peasant
who'd been pushed too far, so she was doomed.

'Bigäíl still tyrannised her
    home and gave her family
        no choice. She vowed revenge
        and packed her crates and
    moved off to a neighbouring
        estate. She
went, dragging her distraught husband
        lagging behind her.
Might as well be a beggar, he thought,

as have to leave his home like this.
  No more trips to la Ciega's,
   no more brooding in the
    zanjón,[19] and no more
   hurrying to answer the
     unbound wheel.
  After all the seed-corn he'd wrung
    from the dirt, there was
nothing left but his wife's tongue, and hurt.

X

Matilde

(Who had a presentiment of doom, and worked as a
cook at the casa grande, and whose extreme ugliness
was stressed by an enormous goitre)

Matilde, Matilde, poor fat
  ugly Matilde, bird of
    ill-omen, mouthful of
      moans. Even her songs
    were a dirge for the scourge of
      the locusts,
  and the growth at her neck was all
    that was left at last
as a scar of a past full of wrongs;

  that, and the limp where the bridge broke
    and hit her, and the rasp where
      a wild cow damaged her
        lungs. Some of the young
      workers saw her merely as
        a huge bag
    of aches and bones, a black sack of
      old cloths and groans. But
she was the ultimate seer of doom.

  For the plantation owners she
    was a cook with a message,
      who brewed narcotics to
        soothe her wounds and who
      saw clear signs of destruction
        everywhere,
    and who thrived on warning and on
      wringing the air. Still,
it seemed wise to keep her gloom in sight.

Matilde seemed to leave bad luck
behind her, and her presence
helped keep their troubles at
bay. Mothers fought for
her visions and her fat frame.
Meanwhile, she
came and went, with her prophecies:
telling the men that
the sap in their backs would waste away;

and the soil would tire, and that no
amount of toil would heal the
cracked mud after the sky
had turned to blood and
the locusts had dropped like a
jointed mat
to flatten and destroy. It had
happened once, fifty
years before, when locusts killed the crops.

Then there was drought and starvation,
only the bananas and
the plantains survived, stewed
grey glue, juice and skin,
and stains on their clothes and hands –
the grey marks
were graveyard marks and a dullness
of the brain, and then
Mendoza filled with the shallow mounds

while Matilde hammered on the
   ground. 'Tilde's misshapen face
      thanked God that she had no
         husband to abuse
   her, and mourned her loneliness
         with the same
breath, with only her aunt and the
   land left, and the drought
was coming, and her aunt was dying.

'Have mercy, Lord,' Matilde used
   to mutter as she kneaded
      the twice-daily mass of
         dough; and again when
   she trudged the long way with her
         wounds to see
her blind Aunt Constancia, lugging
   wages and slowly
hoarded things to lay at her altar.

Matilde lived for Wednesdays and
   this aunt who was secretly
      irked by her. 'Tilde prayed
         as she stirred the black
beans and limed the white corn. 'Have
         mercy, Lord,'
   she cried into the smoking range,
      but He was deaf and
she was left there with her ugliness.

Her aunt could still remember it
  through her cataracts and the
  haze of discontent: the
    vultures were coming
  now, and they would go south and
      Matilde
would be left to grow old with her
  aching foot and the
goitre to cushion her unkissed mouth.

XI

Constancia

(Who had grown blind, and lived on, past her natural
years, nurturing her dislikes while waiting for an end to
her unwelcome life and her niece's unwanted visits)

Constancia, with her blind eyes
     to the sun, dug in the hill
        by bitterness, to life
            itself, outliving
all her heirs and kin but one:
            Matilde,
on her thin strip of slope on the
        High Place, known as the
altar. Virgin of the prostrate womb

and of maternal drudgery,
     Virgin of darkness and the
        waiting tomb; Giver of
            hope who had tricked the
century into letting
            her grope, blind
and aching through its folds, hard-marked
        and furrowed like a
cemetery; tended by Matilde,

visited by crows. Behind the
     frail screen of her unseeing
        eyes the Andes had turned
            soft, and sloughed ageless
in her old age. They'd lost their
            texture in
her toothlessness. From within the
        dim unaltering
eclipse there were only bad Wednesdays,

79

when Matilde came with all her
  offerings to the shrine of
    Constancia's neglect.
     Wednesdays of despair.
  Let the hills erode as the
    flesh had from
her bones, and let the topsoil drop
    into the river
and be dragged away to Mototán.

There was nothing left to stop the
  process. Nothing to be done
   for the grim aunt whose jaw
    hung unbound and whose
  blind eyes searched for some texture
    in the sun,
feeling only water, rain in
   the rains, then thirst, and
in between them, the harsh annual

  mayera,[20] unmindful of age
  or person, ever worse as
    a scourge. Constancia
    took the bitterness
of her ancient entrails and
    brewed a curse.
Curse Matilde with her smother
   and fuss, and curse the
climate that had flayed and dried her thus.

Curse the immortal stubbornness
that held her trussed to the swept
porch, huddled in a heap
like an old corn sack,
made harmless in her last hours
that were years;
years afloat in poor Matilde's
tears as she struggled
with her bloat to please Constancia.

XII

La Ciega

(Who was also blind, but had come to be the richest
peasant on the hacienda, and who made contraband
liquor, and who desperately wanted to see)

He was blind like the grim lady,
  but he grew rich by buying
    black sugar at the mill
    and distilling the
  packed dregs into rot-gut rum:
      fire-water
to ease the toil, and light the eyes
    of all the people
that he knew by name and voice alone,

  who watched him through the bleary mists
    of his own making and earned
    free mugs of moonshine rum
     by describing their
  seen world with sheaths of detail
      to atone
for his abyss. La Ciega had
    so many gold teeth
that a collective pride killed envy.

It was enough to live near such
  a mouth; and then he had a
    wife and fourteen children
    and an orphaned niece
  whom he had protected, and
     la Ciega
had chickens like most men had corn.
    Josefa said that
he owned blankets that he'd never worn.

And then he had fat roan horses
   that kicked and bit, that no one
      could get near to but he
      and his second son.
   Josefa said that she'd seen
         these horses
   bow down on their knees to him, and
      his barrels of rum
turned to statues of Saint Benito

   whenever the soldiers came to
      raid his huts. Benito was
         the patron saint of drunks –
         the only black saint
      in the church – and did such things!
         Even saints
      loved gold, they were told, and Ciega
         had enough for all
of them, he only needed to smile.

   So la Ciega was popular
      and kind, and he lent money
         and gave advice, and he
         could outwit all the
      middlemen from every
            town and bar
   from Mérida to Boconó;
         but the one gap in
his shell was his ceaseless wish to see.

He had been born blind, no one in
his childhood had ever shown
the least hope for his eyes.
But Ciega believed
in miracles, and believed
he would see
before he died; and he was prey
to every quack who
came within slicing range of his face.

All the charlatans and butchers,
cheats and surgeons knew that he
would dig up his bundles
of hidden bills and
pay for whatever cure or
fantasy
they named, as long as they claimed it
would restore his sight
to him – the sight he had never had.

None of them was right or ever
could be, but the failure and
the rack just quickened hope.
So skilled and unskilled
scalpel blades maimed his scarred pits
and he paid
them to dig in his poor sockets.
And Juan, the foreman,
said destiny only teased the rich:

the poor would always have their own
calamities, they didn't
have to buy their pain, it
would come for free like
pestilence and rain. Up on
his outcrop,
though, la Ciega kept trying. While
his wife fed the hens,
new doctors proposed operations.

After noon on Saturdays, all
the men who dared would climb the
steep track to la Ciega's
place and souse their grief
and sorrows in his stock of
illicit
rum, drinking to get drunk and to
forget their wives and
children waiting in their huts, praying

to Saint Benito, the same lord
of drink, to save some wages
for corn and paraffin.
With all the stinting
it bred a special kind of
bitterness,
that Saturday neglect, and a
sort of recklessness
to lure their husbands back from Ciega's.

Some, like Zara, never had to
  try: their men came home and shared
  all their wages fairly
  with their ravaged wives,
  and no amount of strife and
    poverty
could mar their special beauty in
  their husbands' eyes; but
most had to compete with la Ciega's.

And everyone owed him money,
  openly and behind each
  other's back – long accounts
  tallied with notches
  in a stick: a blind man's sums,
    uneven
proof of the natural laws: some
  were rich, some poor, but
all were equal for the Evil Eye.

No one escaped that when it stopped
  at his door. It never knocked,
  it just went in and took
  its toll, and broke their
  everything, even their hope.
    Prayers and
cures were useless, the Evil Eye
  would recognise no
stations at its final toss, just loss.

XIII

Zapa

(Who looked like a toad, and was rescued from a fire as a baby, and who had the most beautiful fingernails in Mendoza, and who was adopted and then turned on to the streets while still a child)

They called her Zapa when she had
   no name; pulled from a fire with
      only rags and burns for
         family. Why she
   was in the hut alone, and
            why it burnt,
and where had her own mother gone,
      no one ever knew.
The Zapa just grew, silent and plain,

   there, beside la Ciega's children.
      Together they gathered cress
         and eggs, and tethered the
            lumpy cow and picked
         up sticks for brooms. A bundle
            of fresh twigs
was needed every day to stuff
      through the used collar
of the sardine tin, and sweep the yard

   and corridor and shoo away
      drag-bellied pigs. Eight years of
         Zapa's life were bound up
            with the brooms. She and
         Elsa, who were closest friends,
            spent hours in
the cool zanjón gossiping on
      sandy stones they named
and rearranged with leaves and grass seeds.

As the years passed, and Zapa grew
   from the rescued child to a
      composed ten-year-old, all
         that she had she had
      by right. She shared la Ciega's
         blood, as niece,
   and that was her passport to love
      and a cotton frock
for nochebuena,[21] and her sandals.

And her food, and a horn comb for
   her hair, her own, not shared with
      Elsa; and, most of all,
         her right to be there
      on la Ciega's clean swept porch
         at six, when
   the silent curfew filled the hills
      and the stray children
all returned like soldiers to their homes.

It was a mark of la Ciega's
   standards that not even his
      sons could wander through the
         evening. There was no
   licence as in the town with
         its scandals
   and the dread Vargas,[22] or Tonta
      María waiting
like a whore. The curfew law was law.

94

No age was too young for it. When
  six o'clock showed by the sun
  and the stream of weary
    workers staggered home,
  la Ciega's children must all
      be with him.
He could not see them but they must
    be there to honour
the ritual and the gathering gloom.

What made the Zapa disobey?
  Elsa wouldn't say ... Zapa –
    so called for a toad, with
    her broad grin and wide
  eyes, and her way of crouching
      on flat stones
like no other child. And Zapa
    spent her rare saint day
money on emery for her nails.

No one had nails like the Zapa's,
  not even the Doña. They
    were Zapa's salvation:
      she was serious –
  she knew about fingers and
      drew respect
for it, and it almost made up
    for her toad-like face.
Why then did she miss that one curfew?

95

Yet, one night, when six o'clock told,
the Zapa wasn't there. Then
seven came, and eight, and
the Zapa's fate was
fixed without her: she was to
be banished
from the house. They allowed for no
excuse. There was shame
now on her name; she would have to go

to save the house from shame. So the
toad-child, Zapa, who had strayed,
no one knew why, returned
and was spurned and her
bundle had been made ready
with spare frock
and comb. At ten years old she lost
her only home and
resumed the status of a fire child.

The plain girl, called toad, had nothing
but her tiny load of beads
and clothes to carry. Poor
Zapa with the seed-
like eyes and stunted hair and
perfect nails,
and no one left to care for her.
Zapa, who had been
to town only to sell herbs and cheese

and once, to see the dancing bear,
and Hercules, the strongest
man in the high Andes,
would go again, down
the long road, with her head bent
in her sin,
to find a life in that market
place, knowing that there
could be no real life away from home,

and knowing that she had done wrong,
knowing there was no return,
and no reprieve; weeping
silently for all
she had to leave – blood and brooms.
The Vargas
was full of such as she. She would
settle there, age and
grow: a child with nowhere else to go.

XIV

Elsa

(Who was la Ciega's eldest daughter, and Zapa's friend,
who missed her)

When Zapa left, Elsa had no
　　friends. She went to the zanjón
　　　alone every day and
　　　　played the games they used
　　to play, but the sticks and stones
　　　　missed Zapa
　　too; and the bright seeds and mosses
　　　　pined in her hands. Each
night she prayed for Zapa at the shrine,

　　and lit a candle to their kind
　　　　Virgin of pain and sorrows.
　　　Crime was contagious on
　　　　the hills, and Elsa
　　knew, however sad she grew,
　　　　she must not
see her banished cousin's face – not
　　　　then or ever, or
she too would share in Zapa's disgrace.

　　Elsa was the star of all la
　　　Ciega's daughters, with her clear
　　　　green eyes and rough blonde hair.
　　　Mano Negro was
　　in love with Elsa. One day
　　　　they'd marry,
she supposed; his anger would be
　　　　romantic after
the tyranny of her father's house.

And so, at fifteen, just three years
   after Zapa left, Elsa
   married Mano Negro.
   He had courted her
in the zanjón. And after
      the drinking
and the dancing and the last pigs'
   chitterlings were done
with, they moved into their own new home.

They had two rooms with new lime paint
   and a swept dirt porch for which
   Elsa would make brooms and
      there were bamboo pipes
to a barrel of water,
      and a hen.
And Elsa had her own stone range
   to blacken; her yard
and her altar with postcards and saints.

Elsa walked the eight miles into
   town to buy her beans and corn,
   then, with the drone of the
      market square still in
her ear, she made her way to
      the red-light
zone. Elsa didn't care for scorn,
   she would track down her
outcast cousin if she still lived there.

But three years is a long time for
a ten-year-old to survive
on the Calle Vargas.
Three years can be the
lifespan for a child whore on her
own. No one
knew where Zapa was or what she
had done. She had come
and gone and disappeared, they told her.

Elsa made her long way home with
her tears, and lit new candles
for her new fears. Then she
waited for her own
children to be born through the
years, hoping
for a plain face, a love of stones,
and a lack of grace:
for the sign of a toad in her womb.

Epilogue

Everyone waited on those hills,
  for the sign of a toad or
   the sign of the cross, for
   the end to illness
  or a day of drudgery,
    and weighing
their loss in the false Roman scales
  that same stone-like pride
that ruled every rock in the valley.

And in all that world of waiting,
  they had dug their nails into
   the slopes of hopelessness
   and drawn flowers: they
  culled seeds, sowed them and waited;
    they made cheese,
and stirred it rancid. For they knew,
  like the colibrí,
poised in the air, how to care and kill.

Their skills were of violence, and
  patience, and mastering the
   knowing silence of the
   sharpened blade. Eyes glazed
  for pay-day while waiting on
    death; watching
for rain, desperate for respite,
  trying to find the
heart to pray for an end to the pain.

Juan was at the pivot with his
    ancient wheeze and his mask pulled
        over his bitterness
        while he fulfilled his
    task: keep the mill-wheel turning
        and all eyes
lowered, and the sugar boiling.
        Together they kept
the valley going on its low hum

    of intrigue and hatred inter-
        woven with the cicadas
        and the river's stone drum.
        With the bare mountains
    above them and the plains and
            swamps below,
    they had to know how to keep their
        footing there, balanced
for ever on their terraced honour.

    With their thin lips matching the chapped
        lips of the hill, they came from
            the monte,[23] the gente,[24]
            the people who fought
        and appeased the land, whose long
                families
    were buried under it up at
            Mendoza, and whose
children were born on the hacienda,

and whose sweat watered it at each
molienda, and whose tears dropped
noiselessly into the
undergrowth. They knew
its arteries and lungs, its
hips and joints.
They had a name, use and knowledge
for each hour, and all
things had uses – herbs must feed or cure,

lure or destroy. Water was stashed
and carried, dung stored, fruit brewed,
grain gleaned and insects used.
Theirs was a land of
wheels and seasons turning and
slicing with
vicious precision. Let no one
stray, and let no one
break the rhythm, and let no one dare

criticise the apparent dull
look in their eyes without first
seeing the litany
of broken hearts that
hung like trophies round their huts.
And because
of the centuries of toil and
because of the still
sacred places in both tree and soil

they grew and shall grow stronger. And
though the oil and the cities
have tried to assail their
ritual wall, they
have survived longer in their
pride and strength
and not surrendered their high place
on the grasping hill:
they live by the strange needs of their will,

and this is their story.

Notes

1 hacienda: agricultural estate.

2 molienda: crushing and boiling of the sugar-cane and juice.

3 trapiche: sugar-mill.

4 la casa grande: the big house, where the plantation owners lived.

5 miche: alcoholic drink made out of sugar dregs.

6 angels: children of age twelve and under are believed to become angels (angelitos) from the time of their death. It is bad luck to mourn them openly.

7 Borbón: a strain of coffee plant.

8 capacho: a bright indigenous flower with medicinal properties.

9 Toddy: a chocolate drink, popular in the Andes.

10 inmortelle: an exotic flowering tropical tree.

11 chimó: a kind of chewing tobacco which dulls hunger and fatigue.

12 Because . . . and because   traditional dirge form when praising the newly dead.

13 la Ciega: the blind woman, but used here as the nickname of a man.

14 verdolaga: purgative plant.

15 escoba: literally broom; a low bush used for this purpose.

16 araguäney: national tree of Venezuela with magnificent yellow flowers.

17 newspaper: when a peasant dies in hospital, his entrails are removed and old newspapers are put in their place to help delay decomposition. Because of the careless way this is often done, the newspapers may remain visible through the badly stitched incision.

18 medianero: a cropper who goes halves with his crop.

19 zanjón: a deep rift carrying water, running at right-angles to the main valley, full here of rare trees and flowers.

20	mayera:	collective term for the many forms of sickness, including often fatal fevers and diarrhoeas, that come in May, at the beginning of the rainy season.
21	nochebuena:	Christmas Eve.
22	Vargas:	the Calle Vargas, name of a street of brothels and whores. No socially respectable woman would ever go there.
23	monte:	bushy scrubland covering the hill slopes.
24	la gente:	the farm workers and their families.